A Child's
Garden of Verses

A Child's Garden of Verses

R. L. STEVENSON

ILLUSTRATED BY A. H. WATSON

THE CHILDREN'S PRESS

LONDON AND GLASGOW

This selection first printed 1968
Cover design by Hilda Boswell
This Impression 1974

ISBN 0 00 166009 8

PRINTED AND MADE IN GREAT BRITAIN

TO
ALISON CUNNINGHAM
FROM HER BOY

For the long nights you lay awake
And watched for my unworthy sake:
For your most comfortable hand
That led me through the uneven land:
For all the story-books you read:
For all the pains you comforted:
For all you pitied, for all you bore,
In sad and happy days of yore:—
My second Mother, my first Wife,
The angel of my infant life—
From the sick child, now well and old,
Take, nurse, the little book you hold!

And grant it, Heaven, that all who read
May find as dear a nurse at need,
And every child who lists my rhyme,
In the bright, fireside, nursery clime,
May hear it in as kind a voice
As made my childish days rejoice!

R.L.S.

CONTENTS

The Child Alone

Garden Days

Envoys

INTRODUCTION

A CHILD'S GARDEN OF VERSES is a volume that we must stand upon a shelf apart; it has to stand alone, for there exists in no language any book that may be placed beside it. None but Robert Louis Stevenson has left behind him, in one small rhyming volume, the key to that locked door which lies between most men and the impenetrable garden of their childhood.

There seems to be three main impulses that stir a poet when he sings of children or of childhood. The first Love—the love of one child or the wide love that embraces all children. The second is Childlikeness—for there remains alive in many of us (thank God) an indestructible child which will at times play pranks or burst into song. The third is Memory —memory so keen that we in certain moods reconquer our childhood's very self.

It is doubtful whether any of Stevenson's verses were written under the first of these impulses. As we read carefully and discerningly these forty-five little poems, we feel that some notes common to all children have been struck, we recognise our own distant emotions and imaginings; the poet's persistent childlikeness speaks to the undying child within ourselves—we respond, we are small again and his playmates; yet, as we read on, we lose sight of our own childhood; it is not with a child's heart that we turn back to the first page and read each verse anew. We find ourselves leaning tenderly, with all the motherhood or fatherhood that may be in us, over one solitary child, a little boy more iridescent than other children, beloved yet alone, timorous yet valiant, frail yet strong, hungry yet satisfied, tender yet self-sufficient, sensitive yet self-secure; a rover at rest, a dreamer in action, whose eyes search beyond sight, whose ears are not deaf to silence.

The child is father of the man; the boy whom we love in this *Child's Garden of Verses* is the vitalised memory of the man he became. Whom indeed could that child become but Robert Louis Stevenson?—and who but he could have brought that childhood back to life? He knew no fatherhood but that of himself, and left behind him an immortal boy destined to win him love far beyond the wide warm zone of his friendships and the short hour of his generation.

When first we enter this garden we do so in a detached mood, perhaps even in a critical mood. We roam about picking out by preference the verses that bring before us visions of our common childhood: *Bed in Summer: At the Seaside: Rain: Auntie's Skirts* (alas! this delightful stanza will mean nothing to the modern child, whose Auntie is no longer sanctified by skirts, but a fellow-possessor of all too prominent leg).

In our search for the accents of universal childhood we probably reject *A Thought: Whole Duty of Children: System:* the note struck in these verses seems a grown-up note, it jars a little because we had tuned ourselves receptively to a key of pure childishness, and here we feel the man interpreting the child. We find ourselves slipping past many a verse that fails to appeal directly to our sense of childhood: *Pirate Story: Travel:* remain unread. Then suddenly the child's voice is heard again:

Of speckled eggs the birdie sings
And nests among the trees—

—we prepare to run out and play with him, but he has already left the garden and wandered away to the sea: he beholds ships and hears the children sing in distant lands. . . .

So we take refuge in a homelier scene.

When I was sick and lay a-bed,
I had two pillows at my head. . . .

Yes, we have all known this. Leaden soldiers or china dolls, we have all peopled the hills of the bed and found comfort in the pleasant land of counterpane:

> *I was the giant great and still*
> *That sits upon the pillow-hill,*
> *And sees before him, dale and plain,*
> *The pleasant land of counterpane.*

The little Louis has caught us by the heart. We have forgotten ourselves and all the other children. We turn back to the first page, hypnotised, and recommence the journey with our elusive playmate. *A Thought* no longer seems too grown-up to us, we find ourselves smiling at our old-fashioned little man; we watch him tenderly as he digs by the sea; we watch him at table schooling himself to manners; and although perhaps, we never played at pirates before, we float with him aboard in his basket on the lea, and let him steer us by a star. . . .

Little rover, whither would you make us follow? Did we not set out to criticize? Come, it is foolish to let ourselves so fall beneath the spell of a child.

Let us start yet again and be properly critical. After all, a man wrote these verses; it is absurd to behave as if we really thought a child had written them.

Yes, we will be critical. What about form? Are these verses very remarkable as poems, anyway? Do they not lack metrical variety? Are not too many of them devoid of the lyrical quality we seek in verse concerning childhood? Most of these verses seem to be spoken rather than sung; and, if we try to sing them, too many seem to fit the same monotonous tune, broken here and there by the tramp of *Pirate Story* and *My Shadow*. *The Lamplighter*, too, has the same tramping lilt:

My tea is nearly ready,
*   and the sun has left the sky;*
It's time to take the window
*   to see Leerie going by;*

—we read on, and are waylaid by memory. Did not children long ago, kneel upon chairs close to the panes on a January evening, hearing the cheerful clatter of tea-cups whilst they watched the lamplighter? . . .

For we are very lucky,
*   with a lamp before the door,*
And Leerie stops to light it
*   as he lights so many more;*
And O! before you hurry by
*   with ladder and with light,*
O Leerie, see a little child
*   and nod to him to-night!*

Why, what's this? In our imagination our face

touches the window-pane beside him as we croon his song:

O Leerie, see a little child and nod to him to-night!

and so we are duly set singing, for here are songs after all, songs with tunes of their own.

My bed is like a little boat

sings the boy; and presently

How do you like to go up in a swing,
Up in the air so blue?

We have begun to discern the music; as we turn the pages to and fro, fresh pulsations and fresh rhythms seize us. Listen, here is a windy night:

> *Whenever the moon and stars are set,*
> *Whenever the wind is high,*
> *All night long in the dark and the wet,*
> *A man goes riding by.*
> *Late in the night when the fires are out,*
> *Why does he gallop and gallop about?*

How the child loves the wind!

> *I saw you toss the kites on high,*
> *And blow the birds about the sky;*
>
> .   .   .
>
> *O wind, a-blowing all day long,*
> *O wind, that sings so loud a song!*

By this time we know how to sing with our playfellow:

> *Green leaves a-floating;*
> *Castles of the foam,*
> *Boats of mine a-boating—*
> *Where will all come home*

He loves the wind, but he loves the water too.

Winds are in the air, they are
blowing in the Spring,
And waves are on the meadows
like the waves there are at sea.

Smooth it slides upon its travel,
Here a wimple, there a gleam—
O the clean gravel!
O the smooth stream!

This child has two kingdoms: the narrow world of home, familiar, kind, and the wide world of his dreams. He was born to rove, the soft fetters of home can only bind the fragile limbs, they cannot restrain the ardent spirit. While around the fire his parents sit, away behind the sofa back he lies in his hunter's camp, singing:

These are the hills, these are
the woods,
These are my starry solitudes.

The home is dear, its warm security enfolds him.
Dear is the hearth; he sings of

Happy chimney-corner days,
Sitting safe in nursery nooks . . .

—the fire-light flickers through
his songs; but from the lights and
shadows of home he escapes passionately
to the wide world beyond:

The lights from the parlour and
kitchen shone out
Through the blinds and the win-
dows and bars;
And high overhead and all moving
about,
There were thousands of millions
of stars

—the truant is seen, chased, and packed into bed:

But the glory kept shining and bright in my eyes,
And the stars going round in my head.

Exquisitely he escapes from solitude:

When at home alone I sit
And am very tired of it,
I have just to shut my eyes
To go sailing through the skies.

A seeker of delight, he finds it everywhere; alone, he founds a kingdom down by a shining water-well, singing:

I made a boat, I made a town,
I searched the caverns up and
down.

. . .

This was the world and I was
king;
For me the bees came by to sing,
For me the swallows flew.

Was ever a child so happy? All the beauty of life out of doors kindles song in him; he sings of the grass:

Through all the pleasant meadow-
side
The grass grew shoulder-high,
Till the shining scythes went far and
wide
And cut it down to dry.

22

—he sings of the hayloft:

O what a joy to clamber there,
  O what a place for play,
With the sweet, the dim, the dusty air,
  The happy hills of hay.

—and when he parts from such joys he parts tearless, exultant:

And fare you well for evermore
O ladder of the hayloft door,
O hayloft where the cobwebs cling,
Good-bye, good-bye, to everything.

What child ever opened a wider heart to the good joys of God's earthly bounty? He sings of:

Happy hearts and happy faces,
Happy play in grassy places.

—he proclaims his faith in happiness:

The world is so full of a number of things,
I'm sure we should all be as happy as Kings.

O joyful child! Like the soldier he hid underground,

He has lived, a little thing,
In the grassy woods of spring.

He has seen the starry hours
And the springing of the flowers.

—he has heard

Under the May's whole Heaven of blue

Strange birds a-singing, or the trees
Swing in the big robber woods, or bells
On many fairy citadels . . .

He is so happy that he cries to the other children
of the world:

Little Indian, Sioux or Crow,
Little frosty Eskimo,
Little Turk or Japanee,
O! don't you wish that you were me.

What is it, then, that makes us feel so tender, so
mother-like and father-like towards this joyous child
who is never sorry for himself?

Alas, there is no life without pain; we know that

he hides his sorrows, that he is too brave and buoyant to recall suffering when it has passed away. (Only to his nurse, who led him through the uneven land, does he speak of the pains she comforted.) Being human and limited of vision, we are tempted to bend in pity over the frail of body, however valorous the soul.

But there is no need to pity this child. Love streamed from his Heaven, and his heart was as a moon that gave back all the light it received.

Now as we close the book, may we sigh:

> *He has grown up and gone away,*
> *And it is but a child of air*
> *That lingers in the garden there.*

—for the man, Robert Louis Stevenson, who wrote these verses from a darkened bed of sickness, made the little fellow that was once himself—that was still himself—live with all that was brightest and least mortal in him.

And live he will, beyond ten generations of children; not, perhaps, to be the playmate of other little ones; rather to fill with delight the empty nurseries of those whose children have grown up and gone away or else have never been. As long as the English language lives, he will live also.

> *. . . Time which none can bind,*
> *While flowing fast away, leaves love behind.*

LAURENCE ALMA TADEMA

BED IN SUMMER

In winter I get up at night
And dress by yellow candle-light.
In summer, quite the other way,
I have to go to bed by day.

I have to go to bed and see
The birds still hopping on the tree,
Or hear the grown-up people's feet
Still going past me in the street.

And does it not seem hard to you,
When all the sky is clear and blue,
And I should like so much to play,
To have to go to bed by day?

A THOUGHT

IT is very nice to think,
The world is full of meat and drink,
With little children saying grace
In every Christian kind of place.

AT THE SEASIDE

When I was down beside the sea,
A wooden spade they gave to me
   To dig the sandy shore.
My holes were empty like a cup,
In every hole the sea came up,
   Till it could come no more.

WHOLE DUTY OF CHILDREN

A CHILD should always say what's true,
And speak when he is spoken to,
And behave mannerly at table:
At least as far as he is able.

RAIN

THE rain is raining all around,
  It falls on field and tree,
It rains on the umbrellas here,
  And on the ships at sea.

PIRATE STORY

THREE of us afloat in the meadow
    by the swing,
Three of us aboard in the basket on the lea.
Winds are in the air, they are blowing in the
    spring,
And waves are on the meadows like the waves
    there are at sea.

Where shall we adventure, to-day that
    we're afloat,
Wary of the weather and steering by a star?
Shall it be to Africa, a-steering of the boat,
To Providence, or Babylon, or off to Malabar?

Hi! but here's a squadron a-rowing
    on the sea—
Cattle on the meadow a-charging with a roar!
Quick, and we'll escape them, they're as mad
    as they can be,
The wicket is the harbour and the garden is
    the shore.

WINDY NIGHTS

WHENEVER the moon and stars are set,
   Whenever the wind is high,
All night long in the dark and wet,
   A man goes riding by.
Late in the night when the fires are out,
Why does he gallop
    and gallop about?

Whenever the trees are crying aloud,
　　And ships are tossed at sea,
By, on the highway, low and loud,
　　By at the gallop goes he.
By at the gallop he goes, and then
By he comes back at the gallop again.

TRAVEL

I SHOULD like to rise and go
Where the golden apples grow;—
Where below another sky
Parrot islands anchored lie,
And, watched by cockatoos and goats,
Lonely Crusoes building boats;—

Where in sunshine reaching out
Eastern cities, miles about,
Are with mosque and minaret
Among sandy gardens set,
And the rich goods from near and far
Hang for sale in the bazaar;—

Where the Great Wall round China goes,
And on one side the desert blows,
And with bell and voice and drum,
Cities on the other hum;—
Where are forests, hot as fire,
Wide as England, tall as a spire,
Full of apes and cocoa-nuts
And the negro hunters' huts;—

Where the knotty crocodile
Lies and blinks in the Nile,
And the red flamingo flies
Hunting fish before his eyes;—
Where in jungles, near and far,
Man-devouring tigers are,

Lying close and giving ear
Lest the hunt be drawing near,
Or a comer-by be seen
Swinging in a palanquin;—

Where among the desert sands
Some deserted city stands,
All its children, sweep and prince,
Grown to manhood ages since,
Not a foot in street or house,
Not a stir of child or mouse,
And when kindly falls the night,
In all the town no spark of light.

There I'll come when I'm a man
With a camel caravan;
Light a fire in the gloom
Of some dusty dining-room;
See the pictures on the walls,
Heroes, fights, and festivals;
And in a corner find the toys
Of the old Egyptian boys.

SINGING

Of speckled eggs the birdie sings
    And nests among the trees;
The sailor sings of ropes and things
    In ships upon the seas.

The children sing in far Japan,
    The children sing in Spain;
The organ with the organ man
    Is singing in the rain.

LOOKING FORWARD

WHEN I am grown to man's estate
I shall be very proud and great,
And tell the other girls and boys
Not to meddle with my toys.

A GOOD PLAY

WE built a ship upon the stairs
All made of the back-bedroom chairs,
And filled it full of sofa pillows
To go a-sailing on the billows.

We took a saw and several nails,
And water in the nursery pails;
And Tom said, "Let us also take
An apple and a slice of cake;"—
Which was enough for Tom and me
To go a-sailing on, till tea.

We sailed along for days and days,
And had the very best of plays;
But Tom fell out and hurt his knee,
So there was no one left but me.

WHERE GO THE BOATS

Dark brown is the river,
  Golden is the sand.
It flows along for ever,
  With trees on either hand.

Green leaves a-floating,
  Castles of the foam,
Boats of mine a-boating—
  Where will all come home

On goes the river
  And out past the mill,
Away down the valley,
  Away down the hill.

Away down the river,
  A hundred miles or more,
Other little children
  Shall bring my boats ashore.

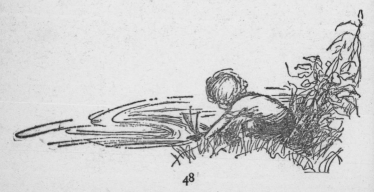

AUNTIE'S SKIRTS

WHENEVER Auntie moves around,
Her dresses make a curious sound;
They trail behind her up the floor,
And trundle after through the door.

THE LAND OF COUNTERPANE

WHEN I was sick and lay a-bed,
I had two pillows at my head,
And all my toys beside me lay
To keep me happy all the day.

And sometimes for an hour or so
I watched my leaden soldier go,
With different uniforms and drills,
Among the bed-clothes, through the hills;

And sometimes sent my ships in fleets
All up and down among the sheets;
Or brought my trees and houses out,
And planted cities all about.

I was the giant great and still
That sits upon the pillow-hill,
And sees before him, dale and plain,
The pleasant land of counterpane.

I HAVE a little shadow that goes in and out
    with me,
And what can be the use of him is more than
    I can see.
He is very, very like me from the heels up to
    the head;
And I see him jump before me, when I jump
    into my bed.

The funniest thing about him is the way he
    likes to grow—
Not at all like proper children, which is
    always very slow;
For he sometimes shoots up taller like an
    india-rubber ball,
And he sometimes gets so little that there's
    none of him at all.

He hasn't got a notion of how children ought
    to play,
And can only make a fool of me in every sort
    of way.
He stays so close beside me, he's a coward
    you can see;
I'd think shame to stick to nursie as that
    shadow sticks to me!

One morning, very early, before the sun
    was up,
I rose and found the shining dew on every
    buttercup;
But my lazy little shadow, like an arrant
    sleepy-head,
Had stayed at home behind me and was fast
    asleep in bed.

SYSTEM

EVERY night my prayers I say,
And get my dinner every day;
And every day that I've been good,
I get an orange after food.

The child that is not clean and neat,
With lots of toys and things to eat,
He is a naughty child, I'm sure—
Or else his dear papa is poor.

ESCAPE AT BEDTIME

THE lights from the parlour and kitchen
    shone out
Through the blinds and the windows and
    bars;
And high overhead and all moving about,
There were thousands of millions of stars.

There ne'er were such thousands of leaves
    on a tree,
Nor of people in church or the Park,
As the crowds of the stars that looked down
    upon me,
And that glittered and winked in the dark.

The Dog, and the Plough, and the Hunter,
   and all,
And the star of the sailor, and Mars,
These shone in the sky, and the pail by the
   wall
Would be half full of water and stars.

They saw me at last, and they chased me with
    cries,
And they soon had me packed into bed;
But the glory kept shining and bright in my
    eyes,
And the stars going round in my head.

MARCHING SONG

Bring the comb and play upon it!
    Marching, here we come!
Willie cocks his Highland bonnet,
    Johnnie beats the drum.

Mary Jane commands the party,
    Peter leads the rear;
Feet in time, alert and hearty,
    Each a Grenadier!

All in the most martial manner
  Marching double-quick;
While the napkin like a banner
  Waves upon the stick!

Here's enough of fame and pillage,
  Great commander Jane!
Now that we've been round the village,
  Let's go home again.

THE WIND

I saw you toss the kites on high,
And blow the birds about the sky;
And all around I heard you pass,
Like ladies' skirts across the grass—
   O wind, a-blowing all day long,
   O wind, that sings so loud a song!

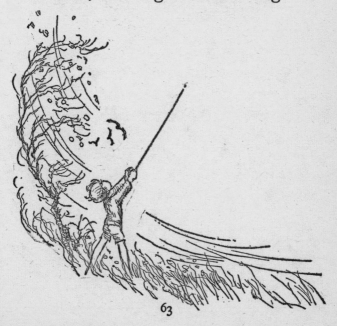

I saw the different things you did,
But always you yourself you hid.
I felt you push, I heard you call,
I could not see yourself at all—
   O wind, a-blowing all day long,
   O wind, that sings so loud a song!

O you that are so strong and cold,
O blower, are you young or old?
Are you a beast of field and tree,
Or just a stronger child than me?
   O wind, a-blowing all day long,
   O wind, that sings so loud a song!

GOOD AND BAD CHILDREN

CHILDREN, you are very little,
And your bones are very brittle;
If you would grow great and stately,
You must try to walk sedately.

You must still be bright and quiet,
And content with simple diet;
And remain, through all bewild'ring,
Innocent and honest children.

Happy hearts and happy faces,
Happy play in grassy places—
That was how, in ancient ages,
Children grew to kings and sages.

But the unkind and the unruly,
And the sort who eat unduly,
They must never hope for glory—
Theirs is quite a different story!

Cruel children, crying babies,
All grow up as geese and gabies,
Hated, as their age increases,
By their nephews and their nieces.

FOREIGN CHILDREN

LITTLE Indian, Sioux or Crow,
Little frosty Eskimo,
Little Turk or Japanee,
O! don't you wish that you were me.

You have seen the scarlet trees
And the lions over seas;
You have eaten ostrich eggs,
And turned the turtles off their legs.

Such a life is very fine,
But it's not so nice as mine:
You must often, as you trod,
Have wearied *not* to be abroad.

You have curious things to eat,
I am fed on proper meat;
You must dwell beyond the foam,
But I am safe and live at home.

Little Indian, Sioux or Crow,
Little frosty Eskimo,
Little Turk or Japanee,
O! don't you wish that you were me.

THE LAMPLIGHTER

My tea is nearly ready
    and the sun has left the sky;
It's time to take the window
    to see Leerie going by;
For every night at tea-time
    and before you take your seat,
With lantern and with ladder
    he comes posting up the street.

Now Tom would be a driver
    and Maria go to sea,
And my papa's a banker
    and as rich as he can be;
But I, when I am stronger
    and can choose what I'm to do,
O Leerie, I'll go round at night
    and light the lamps with you!

For we are very lucky,
   with a lamp before the door,
And Leerie stops to light it
   as he lights so many more;
And O! before you hurry by
   with ladder and with light,
O Leerie, see a little child
   and nod to him to-night!

MY BED IS A BOAT

My bed is like a little boat;
    Nurse helps me in when I embark;
She girds me in my sailor's coat
    And starts me in the dark,

At night, I go on board and say
    Good-night to all my friends on shore;
I shut my eyes and sail away
    And see and hear no more.

And sometimes things to bed I take,
  As prudent sailors have to do;
Perhaps a slice of wedding-cake,
  Perhaps a toy or two.

All night across the dark we steer:
  But when the day returns at last,
Safe in my room, beside the pier,
  I find my vessel fast.

THE MOON

THE moon has a face like the clock in the hall;
She shines on thieves on the garden wall,
On streets and fields and harbour quays,
And birdies asleep in the forks of the trees.

The squalling cat and the squeaking mouse,
The howling dog by the door of the house,
The bat that lies in bed at noon,
All love to be out by the light of the moon.

But all of the things that belong to the day
Cuddle to sleep to be out of her way;
And flowers and children close their eyes
Till up in the morning the sun shall rise.

THE SWING

How do you like to go up in a swing,
   Up in the air so blue
Oh, I do think it the pleasantest thing
   Ever a child can do!

Up in the air and over the wall,
   Till I can see so wide,
Rivers and trees and cattle and all
   Over the countryside—

Till I look down on the garden green,
   Down on the roof so brown—
Up in the air I go flying again,
   Up in the air and down!

TIME TO RISE

A BIRDIE with a yellow bill
Hopped upon the window sill,
Cocked his shining eye and said:
"Ain't you 'shamed, you sleepy-head!"

FROM A RAILWAY CARRIAGE

FASTER than fairies, faster than witches,
Bridges and houses, hedges and ditches;
And charging along like troops in a battle,
All through the meadows the horses and
  cattle:

All of the sights of the hill and the plain
Fly as thick as driving rain;
And ever again, in the wink of an eye,
Painted stations whistle by.

Here is a child who clambers and scrambles,
All by himself and gathering brambles;
Here is a tramp who stands and gazes;
And there is the green for stringing the
　　daisies!

Here is a cart run away in the road
Lumping along with man and load;
And here is a mill, and there is a river:
Each a glimpse and gone for ever!

THE HAYLOFT

THROUGH all the pleasant meadow-side
   The grass grew shoulder-high,
Till the shining scythes went far and wide
   And cut it down to dry.

These green and sweetly smelling crops
   They led in waggons home;
And they piled them here in mountain tops
   For mountaineers to roam.

Here is Mount Clear, Mount Rusty-Nail,
  Mount Eagle and Mount High;—
The mice that in these mountains dwell
  No happier are than I!

O what a joy to clamber there,
  O what a place for play,
With the sweet, the dim, the dusty air,
  The happy hills of hay.

FAREWELL TO THE FARM

THE coach is at the door at last;
The eager children, mounting fast
And kissing hands, in chorus sing:
Good-bye, good-bye, to everything!

To house and garden, field and lawn,
The meadow-gates we swang upon,
To pump and stable, tree and swing,
Good-bye, good-bye, to everything!

And fare you well for evermore,
O ladder at the hayloft door,
O hayloft where the cobwebs cling,
Good-bye, good-bye, to everything!

Crack goes the whip, and off we go;
The trees and houses smaller grow;
Last, round the woody turn we swing:
Good-bye, good-bye, to everything!

AUTUMN FIRES

In the other gardens
    And all up the vale,
From the autumn bonfires
    See the smoke trail!

Pleasant summer over,
  And all the summer flowers,
The red fire blazes,
  The grey smoke towers.

Sing a song of seasons!
  Something bright in all!
Flowers in the summer,
  Fires in the fall!

The Child Alone

MY KINGDOM

DOWN by a shining water well
I found a very little dell,
  No higher than my head.
The heather and the gorse about
In summer bloom were coming out,
  Some yellow and some red.

I called the little pool a sea;
The little hills were big to me;
   For I am very small.
I made a boat, I made a town,
I searched the caverns up and down,
   And named them one and all.

And all about was mine, I said,
The little sparrows overhead,
   The little minnows too.
This was the world and I was king;
For me the bees came by to sing,
   For me the swallows flew.

I played there were no deeper seas,
Nor any wider plains than these,
  Nor other kings than me.
At last I heard my mother call
Out from the house at even-fall,
  To call me home to tea.

And I must rise and leave my dell,
And leave my dimpled water well,
 And leave my heather blooms.
Alas! and as my home I neared,
How very big my nurse appeared,
 How great and cool the rooms!

THE LAND OF STORY BOOKS

At evening when the lamp is lit,
Around the fire my parents sit;
They sit at home and talk and sing,
And do not play at anything.

Now, with my little gun, I crawl
All in the dark along the wall,
And follow round the forest track
Away behind the sofa back.

There, in the night, where none can spy,
All in my hunter's camp I lie,
And play at books that I have read
Till it is time to go to bed.

These are the hills, these are the woods,
These are my starry solitudes;
And there the river by whose brink
The roaring lion comes to drink.

I see the others far away
As if in firelit camp they lay,
And I, like to an Indian scout,
Around their party prowled about.

So, when my nurse comes in for me,
Home I return across the sea,
And go to bed with backward looks
At my dear land of Story-books.

ARMIES IN THE FIRE

THE lamps now glitter down the street;
Faintly sound the falling feet;
And the blue even slowly falls
About the garden trees and walls.

Now in the falling of the gloom
The red fire paints the empty room:
And warmly on the roof it looks,
And flickers on the backs of books.

Armies march by tower and spire
Of cities blazing, in the fire;—
Till as I gaze with staring eyes,
The armies fade, the lustre dies.

Then once again the glow returns;
Again the phantom city burns;
And down the red-hot valley, lo!
The phantom armies marching go!

Blinking embers, tell me true
Where are those armies marching to,
And what the burning city is
That crumbles in your furnaces!

HAPPY THOUGHT

THE world is so full of a number
    of things,
I'm sure we should all be as happy
    as Kings.

THE LITTLE LAND

WHEN at home alone I sit
And am very tired of it,
I have just to shut my eyes
To go sailing through the skies—
To go sailing far away
To the pleasant Land of Play;
To the fairy land afar
Where the Little People are;

Where the clover-tops are trees,
And the rain-pools are the seas,
And the leaves like little ships
Sail about on tiny trips;
And above the daisy tree
   Through the grasses,
High o'erhead the Bumble Bee
   Hums and passes.

In that forest to and fro
I can wander, I can go;
See the spider and the fly,
And the ants go marching by
Carrying parcels with their feet
Down the green and grassy street.

I can in the sorrel sit
Where the ladybird alit.
I can climb the jointed grass;
  And on high
See the greater swallows pass
  In the sky,
And the round sun rolling by
Heeding no such things as I.

Through that forest I can pass
Till, as in a looking-glass,
Humming fly and daisy tree
And my tiny self I see,
Painted very clear and neat
On the rain-pool at my feet.
Should a leaflet come to land
Drifting near to where I stand,
Straight I'll board that tiny boat
Round the rain-pool sea to float.

Little thoughtful creatures sit
On the grassy coasts of it;
Little things with lovely eyes
See me sailing with surprise.
Some are clad in armour green—
(These have sure to battle been!)—
Some are pied with ev'ry hue,
Black and crimson, gold and blue;
Some have wings and swift are gone;—
But they all look kindly on.

When my eyes I once again
Open, and see all things plain:
High bare walls, great bare floor;
Great big knobs on drawer and door;
Great big people perched on chairs,
Stitching tucks and mending tears,
Each a hill that I could climb,
And talking nonsense all the time—
　　O dear me,
　　That I could be
A sailor on the rain-pool sea,
A climber in the clover tree,
And just come back, a sleepy-head,
Late at night to go to bed.

SMOOTH it slides upon its travel,
  Here a wimple, there a gleam—
    O the clean gravel!
    O the smooth stream!

Sailing blossoms, silver fishes,
  Paven pools as clear as air—
    How a child wishes
    To live down there!

We can see our coloured faces
    Floating on the shaken pool
    Down in cool places,
    Dim and very cool;

Till a wind or water wrinkle,
  Dipping marten, plumping trout,
    Spreads in a twinkle
    And blots all out.

See the rings pursue each other;
  All below grows black as night,
    Just as if mother
    Had blown out the light!

Patience, children, just a minute—
  See the spreading circles die;
    The stream and all in it
    Will clear by-and-by.

Garden Days

WHEN the golden day is done,
  Through the closing portal,
Child and garden, flower and sun,
  Vanish all things mortal.

As the blinding shadows fall,
  As the rays diminish,
Under evening's cloak, they all
  Roll away and vanish.

Garden darkened, daisy shut,
    Child in bed, they slumber—
Glow-worm in the highway rut,
    Mice among the lumber.

In the darkness houses shine,
  Parents move with candles;
Till on all the night divine
  Turns the bedroom handles.

Till at last the day begins
    In the east a-breaking,
In the hedges and the whins
    Sleeping birds a-waking.

In the darkness shapes of things,
  Houses, trees, and hedges,
Clearer grow; and sparrows' wings
  Beat on window ledges.

These shall wake the yawning maid;
  She the door shall open—
Finding dew on garden glade
  And the morning broken.

There my garden grows again
  Green and rosy painted,
As at eve behind the pane
  From my eyes it fainted.

Just as it was shut away,
  Toy-like in the even,
Here I see it glow with day,
  Under glowing heaven.

Every path and every plot,
　　Every bush of roses,
Every blue forget-me-not
　　Where the dew reposes.

"Up!" they cry, "the day is come
　　On the smiling valleys:
We have beat the morning drum;
　　Playmate, join your allies!"

SUMMER fading, winter comes—
Frosty mornings, tingling thumbs,
Window robins, winter rooks,
And the picture story-books.

Water now is turned to stone
Nurse and I can walk upon
Still we find the flowing brooks
In the picture story-books.

All the pretty things put by,
Wait upon the children's eye,
Sheep and shepherds, trees and crooks
In the picture story-books.

We may see how all things are,
Seas and cities, near and far,
And the flying fairies' looks,
In the picture story-books.

How am I to sing your praise,
Happy chimney-corner days,
Sitting safe in nursery nooks,
Reading picture story-books.

GREAT is the sun, and wide he goes
Through empty heaven without repose;

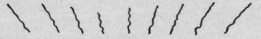

And in the blue and glowing days
More thick than rain he showers his rays.

Though closer still the blinds we pull
To keep the shady parlour cool,

Yet he will find a chink or two
To slip his golden fingers through.

The dusty attic, spider-clad,
He, through the keyhole, maketh glad;
And through the broken edge of tiles,
Into the laddered hayloft smiles.

Meantime his golden face around
He bares to all the garden ground,
And sheds a warm and glittering look,
Among the ivy's inmost nook.

Above the hills, along the blue,
Round the bright air with footing true,
To please the child, to paint the rose,
The gardener of the World, he goes.

THE DUMB SOLDIER

WHEN the grass was closely mown,
Walking on the lawn alone,
In the turf a hole I found
And hid a soldier underground.

Spring and daisies came apace;
Grasses hide my hiding-place;
Grasses run like a green sea
O'er the lawn up to my knee.

Under grass alone he lies,
Looking up with leaden eyes,
Scarlet coat and pointed gun,
To the stars and to the sun.

When the grass is ripe like grain,
When the scythe is stoned again,
When the lawn is shaven clear,
Then my hole shall reappear.

I shall find him, never fear,
I shall find my grenadier;
But, for all that's gone and come,
I shall find my soldier dumb.

He has lived, a little thing,
In the grassy woods of spring;
Done, if he could tell me true,
Just as I should like to do.

He has seen the starry hours
And the springing of the flowers;
And the fairy things that pass
In the forests of the grass.

In the silence he has heard
Talking bee and ladybird,
And the butterfly has flown
O'er him as he lay alone.

Not a word will he disclose,
Not a word of all he knows.
I must lay him on the shelf,
And make up the tale myself.

THE GARDENER

THE gardener does not love to talk,
He makes me keep the gravel walk;
And when he puts his tools away,
He locks the door and takes the key.

Away behind the currant row
Where no one else but cook may go,
Far in the plots, I see him dig,
Old and serious, brown and big.

He digs the flowers, green, red, and blue,
Nor wishes to be spoken to.
He digs the flowers and cuts the hay,
And never seems to want to play.

Silly gardener! summer goes,
And winter comes with pinching toes,
When in the garden bare and brown
You must lay your barrow down.

Well now, and while the summer stays,
To profit by these garden days,
O how much wiser you would be
To play at Indian wars with me!

FAIRY BREAD

COME up here, O dusty feet!
Here is fairy bread to eat.
Here is my retiring room,
   Children, you may dine
On the golden smell of broom
   And the shade of pine;
And when you have eaten well,
Fairy stories hear and tell.

Envoys

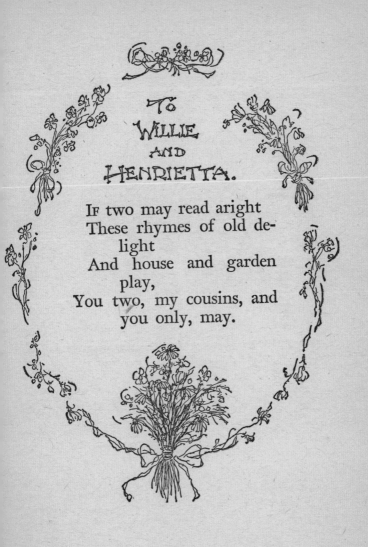

To WILLIE AND HENRIETTA.

IF two may read aright
These rhymes of old de-
light
And house and garden
play,
You two, my cousins, and
you only, may.

You in a garden green
With me were king and queen,
Were hunter, soldier, tar,
And all the thousand things
    that children are.

Now in the elders' seat
We rest with quiet feet,
And from the window-bay
We watch the children, our
    successors, play.

"Time was" the golden
    head
Irrevocably said;
But time which none
    can bind,
While flowing fast
    away, leaves love
    behind.

TO MY MOTHER

You too, my mother, read my rhymes
For love of unforgotten times,
And may you chance to hear once more
The little feet along the floor.

TO ANY READER

WHETHER upon the garden seat
You lounge with your uplifted feet
Under the May's whole Heaven of blue;
Or whether on the sofa you,
No grown up person being by,
Do some soft corner occupy:
Take you this volume in your hands
And enter into other lands,
For lo! (as children feign) suppose
You, hunting in the garden rows,
Or in the lumbered attic, or
The cellar—a nail-studded door
And dark, descending stairway found
That led to kingdoms underground:

There standing, you should hear with ease
Strange birds a-singing, or the trees
Swing in big robber woods, or bells
On many fairy citadels:
There passing through (a step or so
Neither mamma nor nurse need know!)
From your nice nurseries you would pass
Like Alice through the Looking-Glass

Or Gerda following Little Ray,
To wondrous countries far away.
Well, and just this volume can
Transport each little maid or man,
Presto, from where they live away
Where other children used to play.
As from the house your mother sees
You playing round the garden trees,
So you may see, if you but look
Through the windows of this book,
Another child, far, far away
And in another garden, play.

But do not think you can at all,
By knocking on the window, call
That child to hear you. He intent
Is still on his play-business bent.
He does not hear, he will not look,
Nor yet be lured out of this book.
For long ago, the truth to say,
He has grown up and gone away;
And it is but a child of air
That lingers in the garden there.

INDEX OF FIRST LINES